All Stressed Up

Maxine's

Thoughts on Life's Little Irritations

Illustrated by John Wagner

Written by
Chris Brethwaite, Bill Bridgeman, Bill Gray,
Allyson Jones, Kevin Kinzer, Mark Oatman,
Dee Ann Stewart, Dan Taylor, and Myra Zirkle

Book designed by Liana J. Hannsz

The secret to leading a tranquil life is to ignore petty annoyances and save your anger for really serious matters. Like if somebody looks at you kinda funny.

Life is like a long ocean voyage.
It costs a lot and
you're often queasy.